U0098280

流浪基因

吳毅平 攝影集

Born to Stray

A Photo Essay
by Wu Yi-Ping

序

關於流浪與基因的一些疑問

- 旅行、壯遊、流浪、冒險、放逐，是人的浪漫，還是動物的宿命？

- 家裡的貓那麼喜歡看窗外，是純粹好奇，還是真的想去外面探險？

- 家貓會想要與街上的貓交換生活嗎？

- 街貓的野性可以被罐頭或附近居民的愛給馴服嗎？

- 家貓安全但不自由、街貓自由但不安全。那有沒有可能將兩者合而為一，讓街上的貓吃得跟家貓一樣好，過得一樣安全，然後還能隨心所欲的自在晃蕩？貓會覺得這是牠們的大同世界嗎？

- 如果猿猴可以逐漸進化成人類，那貓在幾萬年後會不會有自己的文明？還可以真的養人類為貓奴？

- 有的繁殖場讓貓一直亂生、有人一直想要配出怪異的新品種，這樣會改變基因，讓貓越來越不像貓嗎？

- 明明路上與收容所有那麼多貓，為何還有人要花大錢去用買的。買回家發現有缺陷可以退換貨嗎？被退貨的貓下場如何？店裡賣不掉的貓下場如何？

- 為什麼有人可以在夜市販賣生命？而且還很多人買。

- 有沒有一隻貓待過繁殖場、寵物店、壞人家裡、街上、收容所、好人家裡這六個地方？如果這樣的貓會說故事的話，內容會是什麼？

我只能算是半隻貓，貓的基因裡，我只遺傳了冷淡、孤僻、安靜、陰沉與固執，跟流浪有關的部分學不會，所以我只好跟著牠們，拍下照片，看看能不能知道一點什麼。

Foreword

Born to Stray   *by Wu Yi-Ping*

There is more than one way to shoot a cat.

From the genes of the felines, to the light-sensitive emulsion on the film, photography is still the best way to capture the moment. It documents the elegance and dignity of these stray cats, befittingly.

Since the stray cats are uncontrollable, places where they will next appear is not expectable, shooting their incredible expressions and behavior, in the same place twice, is merely impossible.

There are tons of photo albums, calendars and post cards of "cute" cats, in the shops. But I tried to capture and document everything, about the stray cats, through employing the method of photojournalism—thus; no interfering, no setting and waiting patiently.

I do hope that through my work, viewers will be captivated by the fantasy and enigma of these creatures.

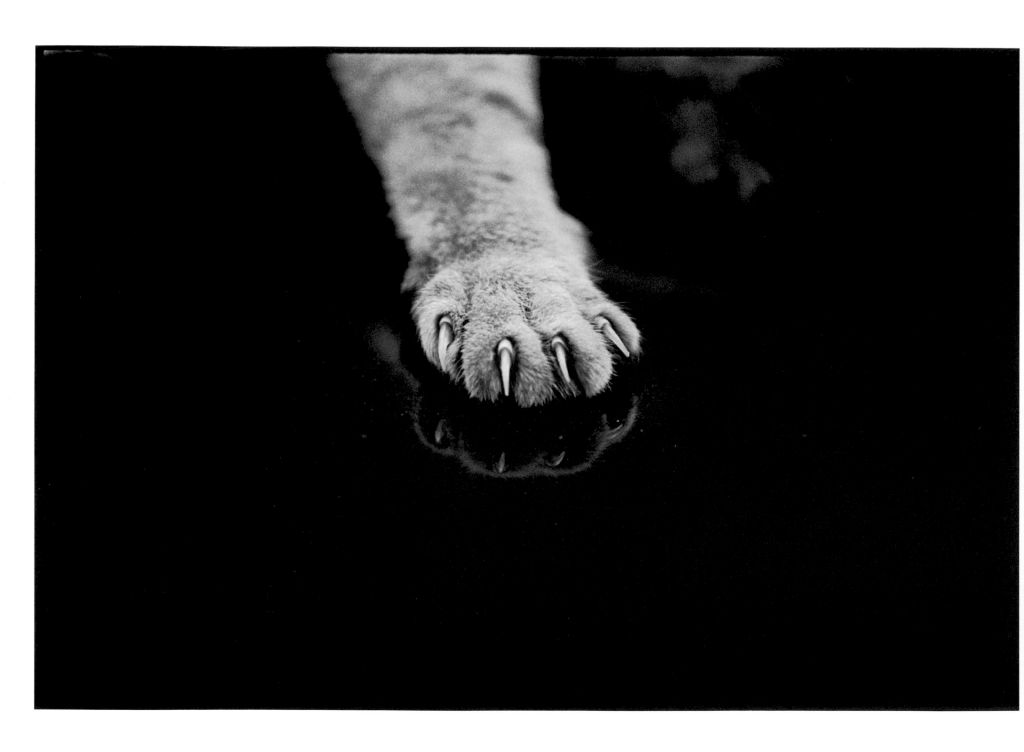

每當有人說： 你們**愛貓人**都怪怪的。
我都回答：其實我比你認為的還怪十倍。

Every time that someone says, "Cat people are odd",
I respond with "Actually, I'm ten times odder than you think"

貓一天要花很長的時間來找到最舒服的**睡覺姿勢**，但萬一找不到，他們還是可以睡很長的時間。

Cats spend a long time looking for the most comfy way to sleep, but even if they don't succeed, they still can sleep for a long, long time.

因為<u>旅途</u>太勞累，所以我們需要舒適的旅館。
因為<u>住家</u>太舒適，所以我們需要出門去旅行。

Traveling is too exhausting, so we need a cozy place to stay.
Our home is too cozy, so we need to travel.

貓是獨一無二的。鍵盤上打注音ㄇㄠ，出來的就只有貓。

Cats are unique. There is no other word in Mandarin Chinese that has the same pronunciation as "mao".

貓流砥柱。

A cat pole....... (kind of.)

男人是外表像大人的小孩；女人是外表像小孩的大人；
貓是外表<u>像小孩的小孩</u>。

A man is a kid who lives inside an adult's body; a woman
is an adult who lives inside a kid's body. A cat is a kid, who
lives inside a kid's body.

狗是驚嘆號，人是句號，貓是<u>問號</u>。

Dogs come with an exclamation mark. People come with a period.
Cats? A question mark.

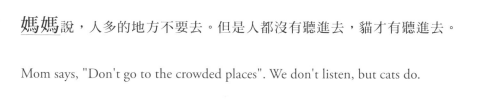

媽媽說，人多的地方不要去。但是人都沒有聽進去，貓才有聽進去。

Mom says, "Don't go to the crowded places". We don't listen, but cats do.

「林中兩路分，一路人跡稀。我獨進此路，境遇乃相異。」（Robert Frost）
只是有時候，兩條路根本從頭到尾都是 <u>平行</u> 的。

"Two roads diverged in a wood, and I took the one less traveled by.
And that has made all the difference." ~ R. Frost.
Yet sometimes, the two roads are parallel.

如果貓會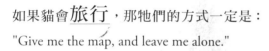，那牠們的方式一定是：
"Give me the map, and leave me alone."

If cats could travel, then they would say:
"Give me the map, and leave me alone."

所謂的**連漪效應**就是，當你養了一隻貓，你的
朋友們也會開始愛上貓。
大家都養了一隻之後，就會開始養第二、第三隻。

The so-called ripple effect: once you have a cat, your
friends then fall in love with cats.
Once everyone has a cat, then they get a second one, and
a third one....

黑貓包，<u>無價</u>。

Black cat handbag: priceless.

全世界最難學的不是中國話也不是俄國話
而是**不說話**。

The most difficult language is neither Chinese
nor Russian, but, rather, keeping silence.

如果十二生肖裡有貓，不知道那一年的出生率會不會
超過龍年。

If the cat was in the Chinese Zodiac, I wonder if the birth
rate in the year of cat would exceed the year of dragon.

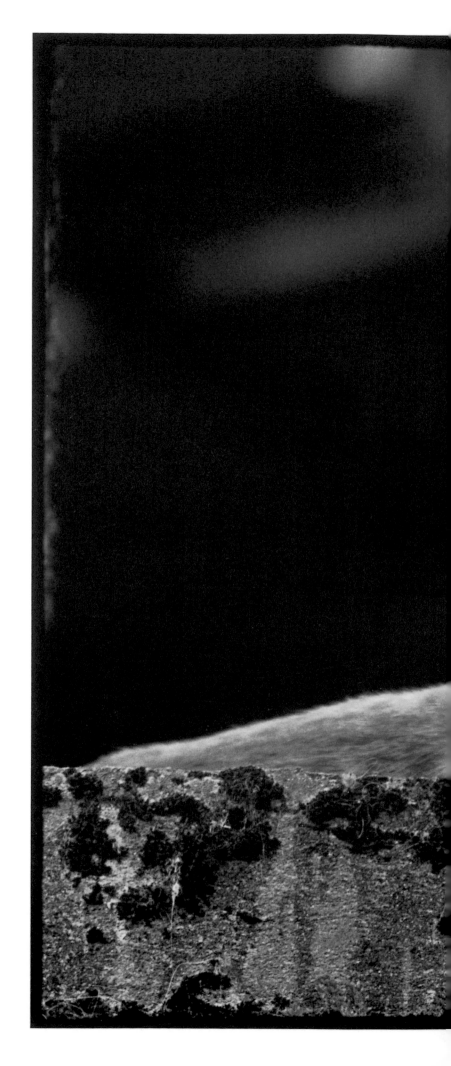

為什麼要去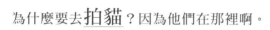？因為他們在那裡啊。

"Why do you take pictures of cats?"
"Because they are there."

八十歲的人，看起來就是個老人；
十八歲的貓，看起來還是像小貓。

An eighty-year-old man looks old. An
eighteen-year-old cat still looks young.

飯後一隻貓，快樂似<u>神仙</u>。

Happiness is eating, smoking and having a cat.

街貓的**肥度**代表著附近居民的氣度。

The weight of the street cats represents the
generousness of the neighborhood.

家裡養過的貓，名字分別是： 小花、小白、
阿醜、阿美、小咪、小貓咪。
姓名學大師，當之無愧。

Leave me alone. I'm only speaking to my cats
today.

壞東西要和好朋友分享。

A trouble shared is a trouble
halved.

貓是很會控制自己<u>食量</u>的，牠們
絕不去吃到飽餐廳。
因為大家在那裡都不是吃到飽，
而是吃到死。

Cats are very good at watching their
diet, so they would never go to an all-
you-can-eat restaurant.
People don't just go there to stuff
themselves; they go to stuff themselves
to death.

抱貓有<u>一百種方式</u>，但最好的方式是不要抱。
找到一隻願意讓你抱的貓算你祖上積德。

There are a hundred ways to hold a cat, but it's the best not to.
If you can find one who lets you hold it, then you've hit the jackpot.

什麼人養什麼狗。
但養什麼貓，就會變成**什麼樣的人**。

Dogs look like their owners, but cat owners
look like their cats.

「鬼見愁」不可怕，「貓都嫌」才厲害。

Boys will be boys.

人會照鏡子，因為他們想讓自己更美一點。
貓不照鏡子，因為他們覺得自己不能再完美了。

People look into the mirror because they want to dress themselves up to look even better. Cats don't look into the mirror because they know they're already perfect.

貓與貓很難相處，他們都覺得人類才是朋友。
人與人更難相處，他們都覺得貓咪才是<u>朋友</u>。

It's difficult for cats to get along with other cats. They think only humans are their friends.
It's more difficult for people to get along with other people. They think that only cats are their friends.

一個出過詩集的朋友想到報社來上班。

我告訴她說：還是不要吧，這個世界，<u>詩人</u>太少，記者太多。

A friend of mine who once published a collection of poems wanted to work in journalism. I said to her "Don't, there are not enough poets and too many journalists in this world"

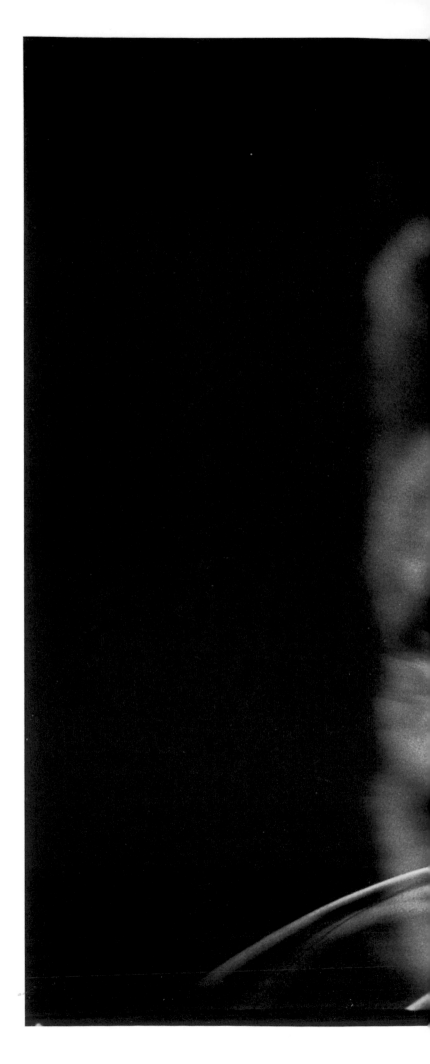

真正的<u>靈魂之窗</u>，
不需要雙眼皮、
不需要假睫毛、
不需要有色隱形眼鏡、
不需要瞳孔放大片。

Eyes are windows to the soul.
Real eyes do not need double eye-lids, false lashes, color contacts,
or circle lenses. They are beautiful just the way they are.

貓沒有九條命，只有九十九種**怪癖**。

Cats don't have nine lives, only ninety-nine weird habits.

可以**溺愛**，也可以維持君子之交。

You can spoil a cat, or you can keep a distance in between.

人的憂鬱，有時連上帝也無解。
貓的 <u>憂鬱</u>，卻只要人的舉手之勞
就能解開。

Even God cannot make everyone happy,
but everyone can easily make cats happy.

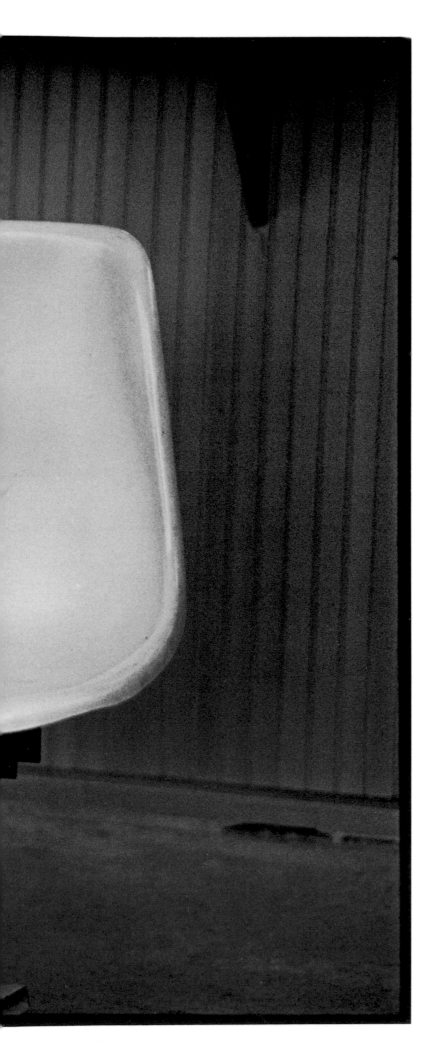

貓很少會站起來，
因為他們知道狗站起來只是為了取悅人類。

It's rare to see a cat standing up, because they know
dogs do that to please humans.

如果貓可以選擇，不知他們會不會想要坐車去<u>更遠的地方</u>。

If cats had a choice, I wonder if they'd like to take a ride to some place far away.

對於貓，我們只有兩樣<u>不懂</u>：這個不懂，那個也不懂。

With regards to cats, there are only two things that we don't get: this and that.

舉頭三尺有**神貓**，低頭三尺有貓神。

Thousands of years ago, cats were worshipped
as Gods. They have never forgotten this.

人在做，貓在看。

Cat is watching you!

佛在哪裡？佛在你心裡，貓在哪裡？**貓在佛心**裡。

Where is the Buddha? He is in your heart. Where is the cat?
It's in the heart of the Buddha.

古人認為，拍照會帶走人的**靈魂**，
事實上是，貓眼會帶走拍貓人的靈魂。

In ancient time, people believed that photography could
steal away one's soul.
Truth is, cat eyes can steal away the photographer's soul.

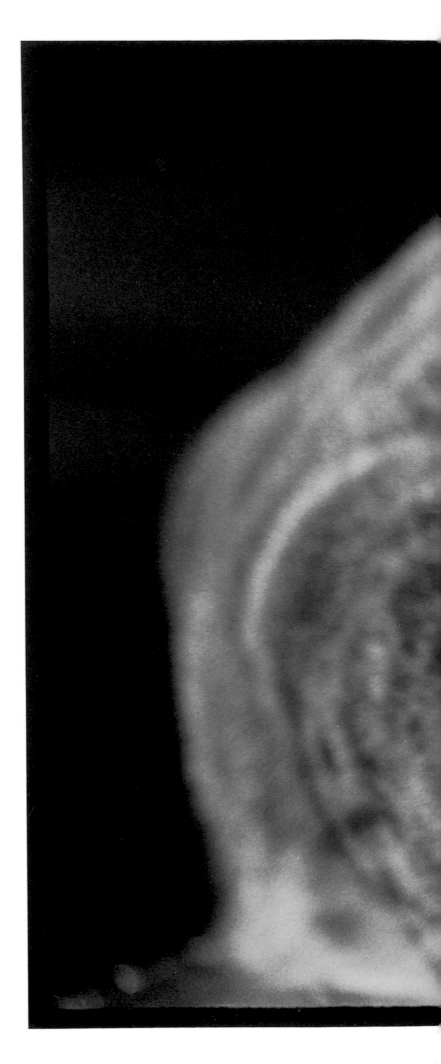

人不爽時所做的決定最爽，貓**不爽時**做的決定讓人不爽。

Don't let the cats make any decision while they are angry.

有人覺得貓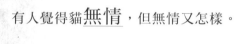，但無情又怎樣。

Some people say cats are heartless, but so what?

野，良貓。

Wild , but well-behaved.

人長舌會讓自己惹來**塵埃**，
貓長舌卻讓自己變得乾淨。

I was normal three cats ago.

玳瑁不是品種，是所有品種加起來的**優點**。

Tortoiseshell is not a breed. Rather, it is the
accumulation of virtue from all breeds

如果你不想為了貓而<u>犧牲</u>某些生活習慣，那是因為你不夠愛貓。

If you don't want to change your living habits for cats, then you don't love them enough.

人與貓的共通點是，都會為了**娛樂**而獵殺。

What do cats and human have in common? They both kill to entertain.

這個世界上只有一種動物可以兼具<u>可怕與可愛</u>。

There's only one creature on this planet that is cute and scary at the same time.

養貓很簡單，只要做兩件事：**做牛與做馬**。

It's so easy to keep a cat. There is only one thing you have to do: work like a horse.

貓從來就**不完美**。
三流的人，才需要完美的寵物。

Cats are never perfect.
Only a person far from purrrfection would need a perfect pet.

貓不喜歡水，但卻能讓自己**永遠**維持乾淨。

Cats don't like water, but they somehow manage to keep themselves clean at all times.

狗覺得自己是人，貓覺得自己是神。同時養貓又養狗的是<u>神人</u>。

If you want the highest seat in the house, move the cat.

一家很有良心的寵物店在門口貼了十個問題，
例如「你的所有家人都同意養嗎？」「你會照顧牠一輩子嗎？」之類的。
我想加上第十一條，「我們真的需要寵物店嗎？」

A pet shop with conscience posted 10 questions at the door.
"Are all your family members okay with you having a pet?"
"Are you ready for a long-term commitment?" and so on.
I'd like to add number 11 "Do we really need pet shops?"

如果小時候的數學題目是**雞貓同籠**，
我應該就會及格了。

For the "chickens-and-rabbits" problem, had it
been cats instead of rabbits, I could've passed
the exam.

要不是每個人都反對，我真的會把兒子取名為**吳小貓**。

I would've really named my son "Kitten Wu" if everyone had not been so against it.

有些人就是要抱著絨毛玩具才能**睡覺**。

Some people always need a fluffy toy to hug while sleeping.

人類好不容易從全身長毛進化到皮膚光滑，但卻開始愛上**毛孩子**。

Although people have evolved from fur to skin, they still love their furkids.

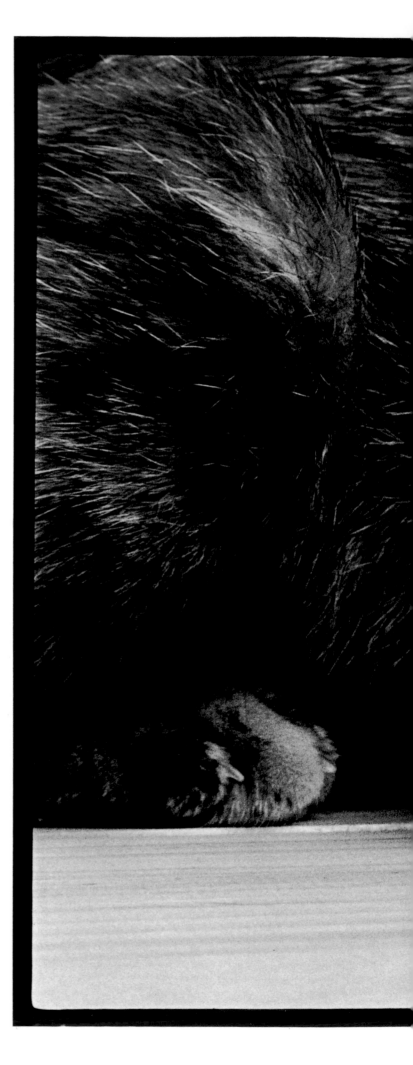

街友需要貓友，**街貓**需要朋友。

A true friend is someone who licks behind your back.

貓的身體為何會香香的？大概是不好的味道都跑到大小便裡了。

Why do cats smell so good? Perhaps all of the bad smell goes into the litter.

人，在屋頂上唱歌；貓，在屋頂上叫春。
歌聲不一定好聽，但叫春一定是<u>天籟</u>。

Caterwaul is the voice of angel from above.

窮得只剩下錢不如**窮得**只剩下貓。

A rich man is nothing but a poor man with cats.

旅行就是去大家都去過的地方，
流浪就是去自己從沒想過要去的地方。

Traveling is visiting somewhere everyone else has been.
Wandering is going to a place you've never thought of visiting.

街貓以為家，家貓以家
為天下，貓奴以貓為天下。

For stray cats, the world is their
home. For house cats, their home
is their world. For cat owners, the
cats are their world.

終於，我發現，自己並不適合當兒子、丈夫與父親，
也不適合當老闆、員工、小開，
更沒資格當一隻貓。
只好當一台**照相機**。

Finally I realized that I'm not really a good son, a good husband or a good father.
I can't be a business owner or an employee. Definitely not qualified being a cat.
So I became a camera.

對我來說，攝影理念可以是任何詞句，但不會是「真善美」。

To me, the concept of photography can be anything, but not reality, purity and beauty.

人類想盡各種方式來取悅貓，貓卻只要維持<u>本性</u>就能取悅人類。

People do everything to please the cats, and cats only need to stay true to who they are to please humans.

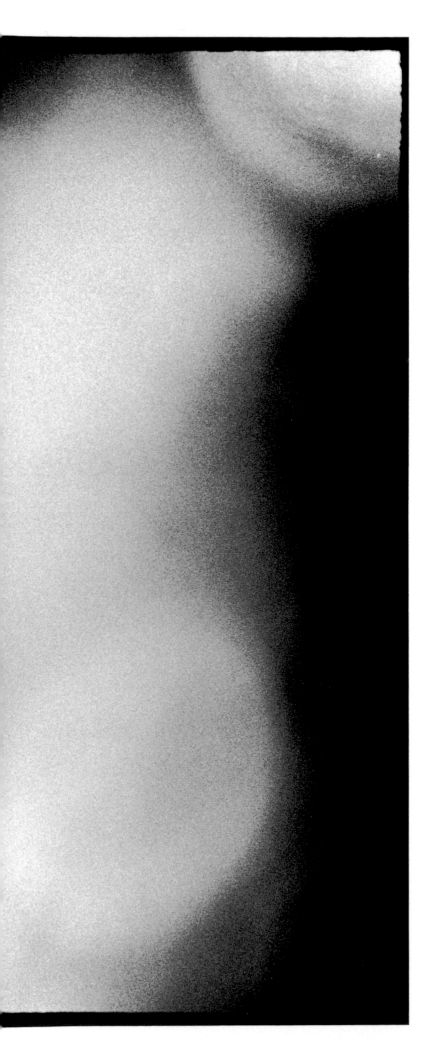

街貓到底是在流浪，還是城市裡的<u>野生</u>動物？

Street cats: stray pets, or wild creatures in the city?

拍攝資訊　KODAK Tri-X 400 ／ D-76 Developer ／ ILFORD Multigrade Paper

凱特文化 文學良品 12

流浪基因 Born to Stray

作　　者　吳毅平 WU YI-PING
發 行 人　陳韋竹 ｜ 總 編 輯　嚴玉鳳 ｜ 主　　編　董秉哲
責任編輯　董秉哲 ｜ 英　　譯　Jackie Lin、Elizabeth McGinsky、Emily Lu、吳毅平
封面設計　萬亞雰 ｜ 版面構成　萬亞雰
行銷企畫　胡晏綺 ｜ 印　　刷　通南彩色印刷有限公司 ｜ 法律顧問　志律法律事務所 吳志勇律師

出　　版　凱特文化創意股份有限公司
地　　址　新北市 236 土城區明德路二段 149 號 2 樓 ｜ 電　　話　（02）2263-3878 ｜ 傳　　真　（02）2263-3845
劃撥帳號　50026207 凱特文化創意股份有限公司
讀者信箱　katebook2007@gmail.com ｜ 凱特文化部落格　blog.pixnet.net/katebook
總 經 銷　大和書報圖書股份有限公司
地　　址　新北市 248 新莊區五工五路 2 號 ｜ 電　　話　（02）8990-2588 ｜ 傳　　真　（02）2299-1658

初　　版　2015 年 4 月 ｜ ISBN　978-986-5882-93-8 ｜ 定　　價　新台幣 630 元

國家圖書館出版品預行編目資料：流浪基因／吳毅平 著 .
一初版 .一新北市：凱特文化，2015.04　160 面；28 × 28 公分 .
（文學良品：12）ISBN 978-986-5882-93-8（平裝）855　104003145

流浪基因

—— 吳毅平 攝影集

Born to Stray

A Photo Essay
by Wu Yi-Ping